D1517319

THIS BOOK BELONGS TO

_____

This book is dedicated to you!
I am honored by all the people who share this
passion to bring black and white images to life.
Cheers to you my friends!

Made in the USA
Monee, IL
01 November 2023

45598655R00066